Haunted Hocking Hills for Kid~
Hocking Hills for Kids
Copyright © 2015 by Jannette

ISBN-10:1940087120
ISBN-13:978-1-940087-12-2

21 Crows Dusk to Dawn
Publishing, 21 Crows, LLC

This book was designed for kids and families in mind. The ghost stories offer places to visit (at the time of print of this book) and places to discover the natural and supernatural world.

Parents: This is a work of fiction. Names, characters, places and incidents either are the product of the author's imagination or are used fictitiously, and any resemblance to any actual persons, living or dead, events, or locales is entirely coincidental. This book was printed in the United States of America.

Disclaimer: The stories and legends in this book are for enjoyment purposes.

Potential Ghost Hunters should always respect the areas to search out the paranormal and also respect those who are still living who might be related to the dead. Call ahead of time to make sure you are not trespassing.

Always check with owners/operators of public and private areas to see if a license is needed to hunt and to check for unsafe areas. Make sure you follow all laws and abide by the rules of any private or public region you use. Readers assume full responsibility for use of information in this book.

Kids, you should never, ever go into an abandoned building or on somebody's property without permission. You should never ghost hunt without your parents or without your parents' permission!

Images:

© *123RF.com* Aleksandrs Tihonovs, Cathy Yeulet, KarenBJones, iimages, Iryna Novytsky, EEI_Tony, Dazdraperma, colematt, WinnebagoPhoto, litoff, Cory Thoman, 3drenderings , Vasily Merkushev, dazdraperma, Denis Cristo, jager Neil Richardson, Morozova Tatiana, Kathy Gold, Mythja Photography SydneyQuackenbush, © Can Stock Photo Inc. / cthoman, Cory Thoman

Children's Animations: NAGISA HAYASHI
Animated Scenes: Colematt

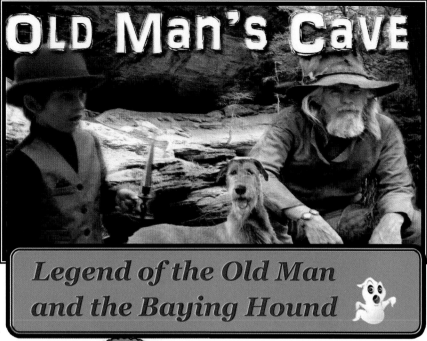

OLD Man's CaVE

Legend of the Old Man and the Baying Hound

Deep in the hills and dark hollows of southern Ohio, there's a special place called Hocking Hills State Park. It is a very large forested area filled with huge trees, high waterfalls, and tall cliffs. Within this park, there is a narrow pocket of land that runs along a rocky creek bed called Cedar Valley Creek. And it is here that there is a long, winding trail leading to a wide recess cave tucked into the sandstone wall of a cliff.

Old Man's Cave

You might see an opossum on the trail.

During the day, many people hike this trail. They come to see the unique rocks and the waterfalls and peer into the cave.

They know they will see common animals in Ohio like deer, opossum and raccoons. They might even spot a black bear wandering beneath the trees. But they don't know that they might also see a ghost! There is a legend here of an old man who haunts this cave and his hound that bays in the surrounding woods during the dark of night.

You might see a frog on the trail.

Or you might see a ghost. . . dog!

You see, many years ago and before the Hocking Hills became a park, two young boys from the little town nearby called Cedar Grove, were exploring the trails. It was a quiet day and no one else was around.

They climbed trees and poked sticks into the creek as kids do. They played a few games and tossed stones at the rock walls. They chatted about the hound dog many heard at night in the old valley they walked now. No one knew to whom the dog belonged and it had been heard baying in the cave for years. Perhaps they would find it and take it home as a pet. Bored and a bit tired, they followed an old dirt trail that led to a small cave and settled down to talk.

Strangely, as they sat on the sandy stone, there was a rustle in the leaves nearby. The boys looked up and were startled to see a man dressed in old-fashioned brown leather clothing, a fur hat and moccasins. He had a long white beard and was carrying an old rifle on his shoulder. A big hound dog with white hair walked by his side. Both boys wondered if this was the hound dog the townspeople of Cedar Grove heard baying at night. But, more important, there was something weird about the man and dog they could just not figure out.

When the old man dressed in leather clothing and moccasins walked past the boys, they thought something was strange.

The old man paused long enough to smile at the two boys. The boys were too surprised by the man to say anything. He had certainly seemed to come from nowhere. They watched curiously, instead, with wide eyes as the strangely dressed man turned slowly and his dog followed at his side.

The mysterious man's soft moccasins and the dog's paws crunched a little in the leaves and sand of the cave as the two walked away. Neither boys blinked as the old man strolled toward a low spot in the cave and stopped. Then, he and his dog simply disappeared as if they had never been there at all!

The old man smiled at the boys, walked to the far side of the cave, and vanished!

The two friends ran home to tell their families about the ghost they had seen. Some rolled their eyes at their tale, believing the boys were making the whole story up. Still, there were a few who had heard old stories of a ghostly man who walked near the  cave. And there had been talk of a hound dog's baying wails at night and the dog could never be found. They were curious too. Eagerly, the boys collected up a couple shovels to dig in the area where the old man disappeared. Perhaps he was showing them that a treasure lay there!

They returned with several adults and soon a crowd gathered to watch them dig up the sand in the dip of the cave. They all wondered what could be hidden where the old man and dog had last been seen. All of a sudden, someone's shovel hit wood with a thud.

A flurry of digging continued until a large box about the size of a man lay before them. Someone pulled up on the lid and all gasped in surprise. Inside, were the bones of a man and a dog! The skeleton was dressed in leather and wore moccasins over the bony feet. There was a rifle tucked by his arm, the same battered gun the boys saw the old man carrying.

A letter found by the man's side revealed that he was a trapper who had once lived in the cave. When he and his dog died one winter, both were buried side by side by his friends who lived in the forest at the cave.

The old man was reburied and such, the folks of Cedar Grove began calling that section of the valley, Old Man's Cave. The ghost of the old man was seen many times by hikers walking the pathway along the creek to the place he was buried.

Hikers still see the ghost of the old man.

He was known to stop and watch them hike as if curious to the reason they were there. And still today, visitors at the park campground report hearing the sound of a baying hound after the trails close at dusk. It echoes up through the valley, a ghostly reminder of an old trapper and his dog buried there long ago.

You can visit Old Man's Cave. The trail to the cave is open from dawn to dusk, closing at dark.

Old Man's Cave
Hocking Hills State Park
19852 OH 664
Logan, OH 43138
39.434686, -82.541574

What's scarier than ghosts in the woods? Poison Ivy! It is a three-leafed plant that grows along the trails and has an oily coating. If you rub up against it and get the oil on your skin, you're going to itch! An old saying is: *Leaves of three, leave them be.*

Trace a route with your finger to help the old man and his dog find his cave.
(answer on page 52)

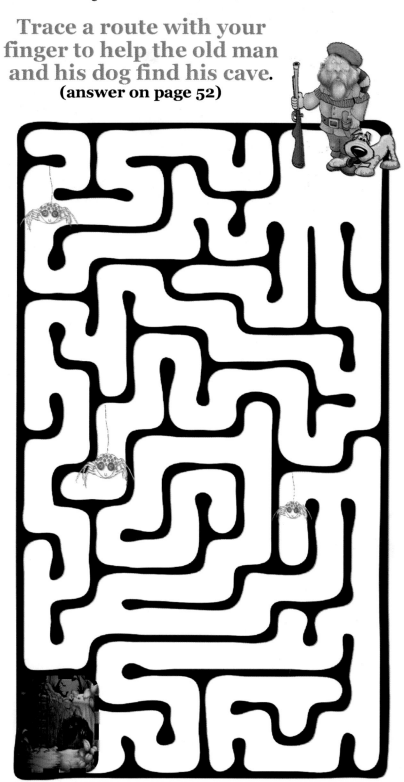

Pale Lady of Ash Cave

Ash Cave has more than one ghost. It isn't surprising. This cave has been used for

Native Indians visited the cave.

hundreds of years by Native Indians as a shelter to rest while traveling. It was also a home for a family of settlers while they built a cabin nearby. Later, many local churches would come to the cave to have their services on nice summer days. Now, people come to enjoy the waterfall and hike the rugged trail.

Some people have reported hearing the sound of ghostly drums in the cave at night. Because the park is closed after dark, Park Officers have been sent along the shadowy trail at night to find the person who is drumming. However, when they arrive at the cave, no one is there!

There is a big, flat stone called Pulpit Rock at the entrance of Ash Cave. Ministers would use this stone as a stage to preach to their churchgoers. Behind the preacher, the church choir would sing. People have heard the sound of many voices singing together even though there is no choir around. Could it be the spirits of long-gone church members returning to sing when they think no one is around?

Pulpit Rock

Did you know that Ash Cave is the biggest recess cave in Ohio? Recess caves are not true caves. They are not underground. Recess caves are formed when layers of sandstone are washed out from a cliff to form a cavity in the wall.

The Pale Lady of Ash Cave has been seen peering out from behind trees.

Of all the ghosts that haunt Ash Cave, the most popular is the Pale Lady. No one knows why she likes this area or who she could be. Hikers who have seen the ghostly woman say she is dressed in clothing of the 1920s. She wears a tan dress that comes past her knees and plain shoes. The Pale Lady is usually seen during the day, walking the trail or peering out from behind a tree. She has even tagged along at hikes led by the naturalist.

You can visit Ash Cave. It is open from dawn to dusk. There is a trail that leads back to the cave.

Ash Cave— Hocking Hills State Park
27291 State Route 56
South Bloomingville, OH 43152
39.395993,-82.545927

The Mystery of the Glowing Ghostly Green Lights at Ash Cave

Yes, it is true. There are glowing ghostly green lights at Ash Cave. Well, part of it is true. There really is something glowing at Ash Cave. But they aren't ghosts. When the park naturalist was told there were creepy lights darting around Ash Cave and they looked like ghostly lights, he investigated.

The naturalist waited until dark, then sat down to watch. Sure enough, tiny balls of glowing green were falling from the trees. Some would stop on a tree trunk, then move quickly up to a limb. Others would float and drift from the tree canopy and disappear.

What could cause these strange lights?

The naturalist cupped his chin and thought for a moment. Then he walked to the tree where the glowing lights had appeared. Suddenly they were gone!

Then he heard a high-pitched *chip-chip*. He knew what made that sound—flying squirrels. He looked around. Near the tree was an old log. And inside the log was a hole that glowed. The naturalist leaned down and looked inside.

A flying squirrel uses the flaps of extra skin on its sides to glide.

He could see that there was a type of fungus found in the Hocking Hills that glowed. There were little footprints nearby. Ah ha! The flying squirrels had crawled into the hole in the log and were now covered with the GLOWING FUNGUS!

It was not ghosts at all. Sure enough, glowing flying squirrels had invaded the trail. After rolling around in the fungus, they glowed an eerie green. The little squirrels had climbed their way to the tops of the trees, then used flaps on their skin to glide from limb to limb. Then, the little squirrels soared from tree to tree.

Mystery solved!

Real glowing fungus found in the woods at night.

Is it a ghost or is it something else?

There are many birds and mammals that roam the woods at night. Sometimes, the sounds they make scare people and they think they are hearing ghosts.

Screech Owl

The Screech Owl's whistle is like a high-pitched scream.

Raccoon

Raccoons exploring creeks for crawdads to eat turn over stones and make clicking sounds.

White-tailed Deer

Deer walking in the grass and brush sound like ghostly footsteps. They make a husky snorting sound like a sneeze when scared.

Legend of the Thieves' Cave

With a nickname like Thieves' Cave, it is not hard to imagine the kind of ghosts found inside this small recess cave just off the trail at Conkle's Hollow Nature Preserve. Tradition holds that long ago, a band of Native Indians would rob settlers traveling their way along the rivers and creeks in this part of Ohio. At this time, the land was thick with trees. The place where Conkle's Hollow is now was hidden within a deep forest. The only people who knew of this secret cave were the few Shawnee who would stash their stolen loot inside.

One day, the thieves came upon a small boat of pioneers nearby. They swooped in to steal their supplies. Settlers hiding behind trees ambushed the Native Indians.

The thieves were chased through the woods and along the trails. They only stopped when they were cornered in the hollow near their cave. Realizing their mistake, the Shawnee tried to climb the walls to escape. But they were caught. Legend tells they were hung in the cave.

Now, they return in ghostly form to protect their stolen treasure hidden somewhere near the cave. Tiny spirit lights are seen at the cave bobbing up and down. You can visit the Thieves' Cave (also called Horsehead Grotto) from dawn to dusk:

Conkle's Hollow State Nature Preserve
24132 Big Pine Road
Rockbridge, OH 43149
39.453492, -82.572727

HOCKING HILLS KOA

A Haunting at Blackjack

At one time, a town called Blackjack once stood where the Hocking Hills KOA campground is now. It was big enough to have a post office, a church and a market. Although the town is now gone, there are two things from its past that still remain—a cemetery and a ghost that visits the graves within.

A shadowy figure has been seen walking along the roadway at the campground and to the small cemetery. It stops for just a moment in front of the graves within. Then it disappears. It is believed to be the ghost of a young woman who lived in Blackjack named Aryanne. It is near her grave the shadowy figure seems to vanish.

No one knows the reason she visits her grave. Some believe she returns to look for the rest of her family. There are no graves for her brothers, sisters, mom or dad there.

The Hocking Hills KOA has many fun things to offer. There is a swimming pool, gift shop, playground and even a gem mine where kids can pan for pretty stones. The ghost that lives at the campground is quiet and keeps to herself. Most campers will never know she is around. Perhaps they will only see her shadow out of the corner of their eye and think it is nothing more than another person walking around.

If you get to visit the campground, keep an eye out for Aryanne. You might see her shadow walk by. And if you do, perhaps you can stop her for just a moment. You can ask Aryanne why she returns to the little cemetery once in a while.

You can visit the KOA at:
Logan/Hocking Hills KOA
Collison Cemetery
29150 Pattor Road
Logan, OH 43138
39.468286,
-82.489368

Ghost hunt at Aryanne's grave at Blackjack Cemetery. Above, Lori Hoffstetter, co-owner of Hocking Hills KOA investigates with campers.

State Route 56 Ghost Car

While heading down State Route 56 late one night to patrol Ash Cave, a park officer passed a car with a flat tire slowly creeping its way along the road. When he turned his cruiser around to help the driver, the car had completely disappeared.

It wasn't the first time this ghost car had appeared. Volunteer firemen and sheriff deputies have come to the aid of the motorist with a flat tire in that area, only to see the car vanish.

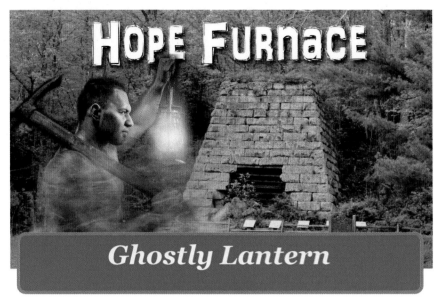

Ghostly Lantern

In the 1800s, a furnace for making iron was built where Lake Hope State Park now stands. The men who worked there brought their families and a town was built for them to live in called Hope Furnace. There was a school, a store and little cabins not far from the furnace.

Hope Furnace looked much like this iron furnace when it was working.

When the furnace was in use, a worker kept guard at the top of the rock oven to make sure the fire inside used to melt the iron kept burning. To guide his way in the darkness, he carried a lantern.

There is a legend passed down that one of these workers fell into the fiery furnace on a dark, stormy night. After his death, people in the town would see a ghostly lantern hovering near the building on nights when lightening lit the sky. Even nowadays, people driving past the iron furnace at night have reported seeing a lantern light bobbing along the top of the crumbling stone furnace.

You can visit Hope Furnace:

27331 State Rte 278, McArthur, OH 45651

39.331741, -82.340341

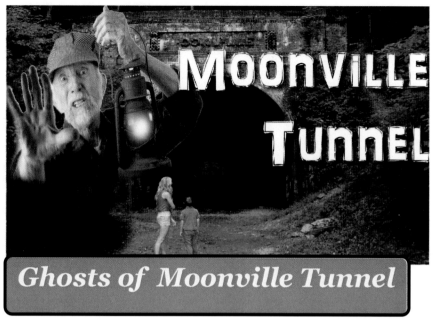

Ghosts of Moonville Tunnel

There was a time when southern Ohio had many little towns popping up so men could work at local coal mines and their families had a place to live nearby. Moonville was a town that started just like this. It had homes, a schoolhouse, a gristmill to grind grain into flour, saloons and a cemetery. It also had a train track that ran straight through a tunnel dug into a hillside.

Moonville Tunnel

The Moonville Engineer

But along with the railroad barreling through the town, there also came deaths because of its trains. On a cold November night in 1880, a train was coming along the tracks and it ran into another train. The engineer that guided the train and the fireman who kept it running were both killed. Fifteen years after the wreck, a tall figure dressed in a white robe and carrying a lantern was seen near the tunnel. The ghostly figure had a long, white beard and the eyes glistened like two balls of fire. Since then, people have seen the ghostly form. Others have taken pictures of a figure standing near the back of the tunnel that looks like a train engineer with a tall hat and wearing a suit.

The Moonville Brakeman

The brakeman for the railroad was usually a younger man. His job was to stand on top of the train and turn a wheel to help the train come to stop. He carried a lantern with him at night to see where he was going and to signal an emergency to the engineer.

It was a dangerous job perched on top of a moving train. Many times the young brakemen would have to run on top of one car roof and jump to the next to apply brakes to another train car. It was not uncommon when the train began to jerk to a stop for a brakeman to lose his balance and fall between the cars and under the wheels.

There were four brakemen who died in Moonville performing their dangerous job. The railroad is no longer in use. But when it was, railroad engineers running the tracks at night from Marietta to Cincinnati claimed to see a man with a lantern waving at them. It was a lonely, dark stretch of railroad known for rock falls. Believing that there was something dangerous ahead on the tracks, the engineers desperately pulled the train to a stop. When they did, the lantern light completely vanished.

Was it the ghost of the brakeman the train engineers saw? We may never know, but even today, people see the orange glow of a lantern light waving back and forth along the tracks. When they try to chase it down, it completely disappears near the Moonville Tunnel and cannot be found.

A real picture of the Moonville Ghost.

Moonville's Lavender Lady

The town of Moonville was located between the towns of Mineral and Hope Furnace. The old dirt roads connecting these towns went up and down many steep hills. They were difficult to walk and were busy with mule and horse carts. They were also deeply rutted by the wagon wheels.

The railway tracks, however, were pretty straight. They also ran from town to town. So the trains would not have to pull heavy cargo up high hills, tunnels were dug right through them. In fact, because they provided such a direct route, many people walked the tracks from Moonville to Hope Furnace and Mineral.

Sometimes, though, those walking the train tracks did not hear or see the trains. One day, an old woman walking along the tracks was killed by an oncoming train near the far end of Moonville Tunnel. After her death, many people would catch the scent of the lavender perfume she would wear. It weaves in and out of the woods and along the overgrown trails.

The trail is rugged. It has lots of mosquitos and poison ivy! Bring bug spray!

Now all that is left of the old town of Moonville are a few big fieldstones, a well and the tunnel. The old rail trail is not maintained and is overgrown with plants. The train trestle that once crossed nearby Raccoon Creek is gone. You can still come and visit the town once bustling with people. You can explore the tunnel and try to see the ghosts of its past. Well, that is, if you dare!

You can visit Moonville Tunnel:

Hope-Moonville Road, McArthur, OH 45651 (moonvilletunnel.net)39.310648, -82.324612

MATCH THE GHOST WITH THE AREA IT HAUNTS!

(answer on page 52)

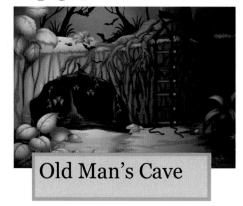

Old Man's Cave

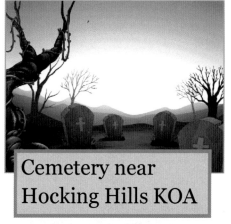

Cemetery near Hocking Hills KOA

Moonville Tunnel

Kings Station Ghost Town

The tiny village of Kings Station was built around the Cincinnati and Marietta Railroad. It had a few homes, a schoolhouse and a general store. Like many of the railway towns in the hilly sections of southern Ohio, it had its own tunnel. And of course, it has a ghost.

King Tunnel along Athens Rails to Trails.

In the 1800s, a young man was walking the railway home at night from the town of Mineral to Hope Furnace. His father and mother were meeting him halfway so he did not have to walk alone in the dark. Between the two towns, was Kings Station.

When he passed through the tunnel there, he saw that a young woman was walking ahead of him. He thought he recognized her as a friend he knew from Mineral. He tried to call out to her, but she did not listen. The faster he walked, the faster she walked. Then, suddenly, she disappeared in a wisp of mist.

Frightened, the young man continued on at a very fast pace. Later, he found out that on the night he saw the ghostly woman, it was the same night his friend from Mineral had died. Others saw this young woman, too, through the years.

Nowadays, you can walk the same railroad track along the Athens Rails to Trails through the town of Kings Station. Little remains but the gravel railroad path and the wooden tunnel. And, of course, if you are lucky, there might even be a ghost!

You can visit Kings Station and the Tunnel:

Athens County Rail Trail

Trail head parking: 1035-1043 Rockcamp Rd

New Marshfield, OH 45766

39.319876, -82.284522

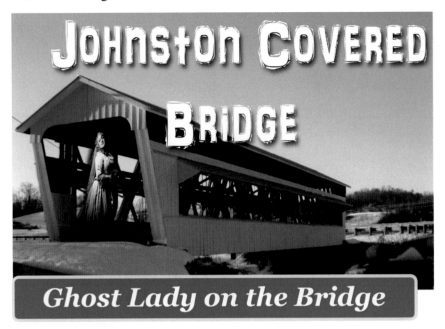

Johnston Covered Bridge

Ghost Lady on the Bridge

When carriages were more common on roads than cars, covered bridges were built so people could cross rivers and streams. During this time, the Johnston Covered Bridge was built over Clear Creek. Over the years, many people crossed over the bridge either by foot, by carriage or on horseback.

If you talk to someone who lives near the Johnston Covered Bridge, they may tell you it is haunted. A ghostly woman has been seen strolling along the old, wooden floor. Sometimes, she stops and waves. Other times, she simply stares at those passing by.

A ghostly woman waves.

The Johnston Covered Bridge is haunted by a woman who waves at people passing by on the road.

Local legends reveal she was a woman who drowned in the creek during a flood while trying to cross. You can try to see her too. Although the bridge is closed to cars, it is open for people to walk across. And if you do, give her a wave. She just might greet you in return.

You can visit the bridge:
Johnston Covered Bridge
Clearcreek Road (County Hwy 69)
off McDonald Road SW
Lancaster, OH 43130
39.613445, -82.658803

Witch Rock

One of the cool features of the Hocking Hills Region are huge rocks. There is a place where you can see one of these that is supposed to be used by local witches. It is along the roadway driving through Clear Creek Metropark. It is said that if you pass this big rock and there are sticks lined up beneath it, you may not want to go farther. It is a warning from the witches that they do not want you to pass this way along the road. You can see Witch Rock:

Clear Creek Metro Park

185 Clear Creek Road,Rockbridge, OH 43149

39.591998, -82.58337

Mathias Cabin Ghosts

The Mathias Cabin was owned by the same family for many years. Then, they gave it to Clear Creek Park. Hikers who have stopped to look at the Mathias Cabin tucked along the edge of the woods at Clear Creek Metro Park have heard mysterious voices and laughter. Some have seen items move on the porch and inside the cabin even when there is no wind blowing. Cars driving by the cabin at night have also reported strange lights inside the cabin. There have also been reports of someone waving from the windows at cars passing by!

You can see the cabin at Clearcreek Metro Park:

185 Clear Creek Road Rockbridge, OH 43149

39.597108,-82.555432

How many ghosts can you count? Which ghost is different than the others?

(answer on page 52)

Hermit of Allen Knob

There once was an old hermit who lived alone on a hill called Beck's Knob. Each day, he would walk from Beck's Knob along an old dirt roadway and across a bridge that spanned a creek named Hunter's Run. He was heading to another hill nearby called Allen Knob. There, he would climb to the top of Allen Knob and read his bible during the day. At night, he would return the same route down the hill, along the road, across the bridge and up the second hill to his home at Beck's Knob.

If you were to stand on the roadway a hundred years ago, you might see the old hermit walking from one hill to the next. The hermit died one night. Before he died, he asked to be buried in a grave on Allen Knob where he loved to read. No one knows if he was buried there or not. Still, his ghost has been seen walking the route down from Beck's Knob, along the roadway, across Hunter's Run Bridge and up Allen Knob hill where he loved to read.

You can visit Allen's Knob and hike the trail to the top to look for the ghost at:

Shallenberger State Nature Preserve

2468-2598 Becks Knob Rd SW

Lancaster, OH 43130

39.691446, -82.657781

Bloody Horseshoe Grave

James was a farmer who grew up in a small town. When he got to the age he wanted to find a wife, two young women

caught his eye. One was named Mary and the other, Rachael. Both were pretty and fun to be around. James could not make up his mind which young woman he would marry. But one night while riding his horse home, he fell to sleep. When he awakened, the horse was standing outside Mary's door.

James believed that it was a sign that he should marry Mary. On a cold January in 1844, the two were wed. It was tradition for the parents of both newlyweds to give them a gift they could use to start their lives together. From both sides of the family, the young couple received one handsome workhorse, so they had a team of horses to start their own farm. With those two horses, Mary and James did build a home and start a farm. They were happy together for a little more than a year until Mary died. She was buried in a corner plot at Otterbein Cemetery. Sadly, James placed a marker on her grave and worked hard on his farm. But he did not return the horse Mary's family had given the two as a wedding gift.

Three years later, James married the sweetheart he had not chosen first, Rachael. During this time, it was whispered that James had broken the tradition by not returning the horse to Mary's parents after she died.

Still, James kept the horse. He was happy with his new wife. The farm was doing quite well. All would seem perfect except for one small thing. When James visited his first wife's grave he saw a bloody red shape of a horseshoe on the headstone! Was it a reminder he had not returned the horse?

James and Rachael lived long happy lives and had children. But the grave with the horseshoe would always be on their minds.

Mary's grave-front

Mary's grave-back

The grave is still located at the little cemetery. If you are very careful and quiet, you can stop in and take a look at the stone. And you can see for yourself the bloody horseshoe on the back and decide if it was left by a ghost.

You can see the cemetery at:
Otterbein United Methodist Church Cemetery
County Road 62/ Otterbein Road Northwest
Rushville, OH 43150
39.77194, -82.36333

More. . .is it a ghost or is it something else?

There are many animals in the Hocking Hills that make strange and scary noises. Some are screams, some sound like laughter and others even sound like they are saying "Boo!"

The bobcat has a high-pitched scream that sounds like a witch cackle.

Coyotes shriek, yelp and howl.

Barred Owls make a low, hooting sound like a ghost. They even make a laughing cackle if another owl trespasses on their territory.

Ghost Hunting and
Ghost Hunting Tools

Telling ghost stories and trying to find ghosts is fun. It is another way to discover the outdoor world. Most people who hunt for ghosts believe that spirits are formed by *energy*. The equipment they use to find the spirits, then, are the same kinds of tools people use to detect different kinds of energy in the world around them.

So how do you ghost hunt? Just find a safe place that is supposed to be haunted. Make sure your parents know where you are and that you are supervised. You can use simple tools you have around your house to hunt. Cell phones can take pictures. Digital recorders tape sounds that you cannot hear, but are picked up on the recorder. You can ask questions like: "What is your name?" or "Are you a boy or a girl?" If you feel uncomfortable or get scared, you can simply stop and walk away.

Want to know more about ghost hunting tools? Just go to the next page!

GHOST HUNTING TOOLS
BY PAT QUACKENBUSH

Digital Recorders: Ghostly sounds such as talking, knocking, crying, laughter or even whistling are all things that our ears can hear. But we now know that many ghosts can make sounds that are very high or low and our ears may not be able to pick them out. Digital voice recorders are used to hear ghostly things that might not be heard with our own ears.

Thermometers: Thermometers detect heat energy and can show the user if there is

a big temperature change. During a ghost hunt, many hunters look for what is called a *cold spot*. Ghosts can use energy from heat to help form a sound, move an object, or make themselves visible so we can see them.

Cameras/Video Recorders:

Cameras and video recorders allow the user to see things in dark places where their own eyes cannot see. It also helps prove things one person's eyes do see, but someone else's eyes did not. We can show the picture to prove what we saw was not just a trick of the light or a stray shadow caused by something moving in the wind. Using a camera is one way to stop a moment in time and freeze small details our eyes and brains may have missed.

Ghost Tools You can Make At Home

A few tools to detect ghosts can be made from items found around your house. A great ghost hunting tool is a piece of quartz crystal hung on a string or chain. When the crystal gets near a ghost it will slowly swing or circle.

Another kind of detector is called a  *dousing rod.* All you need is a couple of wire clothes hangers. You can have an adult help you cut and bend a clothes hanger into a large *L*-shaped rod. *Watch out for pointy ends!* Hold the short handle in your fist and aim the longer straight end outward. You will need two rods, one for each hand. Then hold your handle end and leave the other longer end sticking out straight away from your body. Hold the two rods and your hands a little apart. Walk slowly forward and when the rods find a ghost they will cross. Remember, dousing rods also pick up water and electric. So they are unreliable overtop creeks, on bridges or near electric power.

Another tool you can use for ghost hunting would be a rubber ball. Lay it on a flat surface and back away. A ghost just might push it and make it roll.

ANSWERS:
MATCH THE GHOST WITH THE AREA IT HAUNTS!

Moonville Tunnel

Cemetery near Hocking Hills KOA

Old Man's Cave

THE TRAIL:

HOW MANY GHOSTS?
THERE ARE 27 GHOSTS.

This is the ghost that is different.

67973294R00031

Made in the USA
Columbia, SC
03 August 2019